Grandmother's Memories

Reflections & Remembrances

Lineage

My grandmothers were strong.
They followed plows and bent to toil.
They moved through fields sowing seed
They touched earth and grain grew.
They were full of sturdiness and singing
My grandmothers were strong.

My grandmothers are full of memories
Smelling of soap and onions and wet clay
With veins rolling roughly over quick hands
They have many clean words to say.
My grandmothers were strong.
Why am I not as they?

MARGARET WALKER

Grandmother's Memories

Reflections & Remembrances

WRITTEN AND COMPILED BY DEBORAH LATIMER

DESIGNED AND PHOTOGRAPHED BY ROBYN LATIMER

LANSDOWNE

Published by Lansdowne Publishing Pty Ltd
Level 1, 18 Argyle Street, The Rocks, Sydney NSW 2000, Australia

First published 1998

ISBN 1 86302 619 3

Printed in Singapore by Tien Wah Press Pte (Ltd)

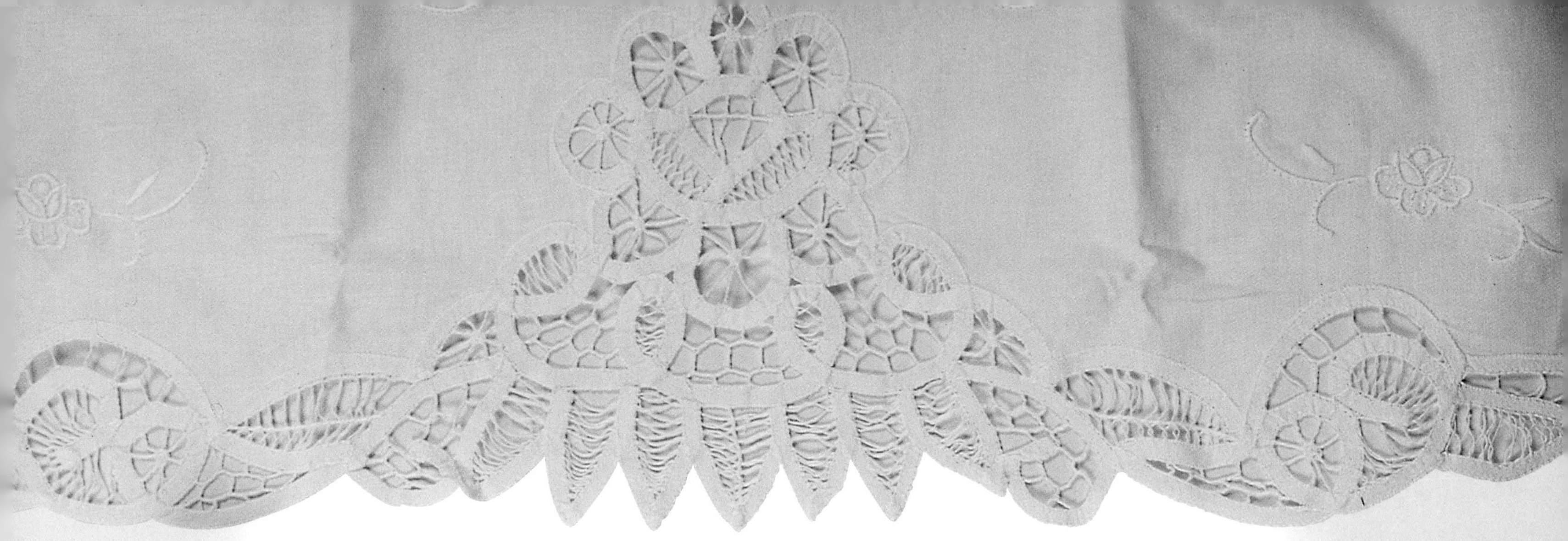

I dedicate this book to:

....

....

I love thee with the breath,
Smiles, tears, of all my life!

ELIZABETH BARRETT BROWNING

CONTENTS

WHY THIS BOOK IS FOR YOU, MY GRANDCHILD

We'll talk of sunshine and of song,
And summer days when we were young;
Sweet childish days that were as long
As twenty days are now.

WILLIAM WORDSWORTH

YOUR BIRTH

Your birth date ....

....

Time of birth ....

....

Your place of birth ....

....

A special moment ....

....

What I said about you ....

....

What I said about you

A day it was when I could bear
Some fond regrets to entertain;
With so much happiness to spare,
I could not feel a pain.

WILLIAM WORDSWORTH

To see a World in a Grain of Sand
And a Heaven in a Wild Flower,
Hold Infinity in the palm of your hand
And Eternity in an hour.

WILLIAM BLAKE

A little about me, your grandmother

My names ....

....

My birthday ....

....

My birthplace ....

....

My star sign ....

....

My birthstone ....

My birthflower ....

So that you may know me

[PHOTOGRAPH]

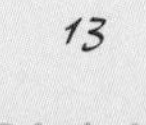

OUR FAMILY TREE

Maternal

YOUR GREAT GRANDMOTHER

Names

Birthdate

Birthplace

YOUR GREAT GRANDFATHER

Names

Birthdate

Birthplace

YOUR GRANDMOTHER

Names

Birthdate Birthplace

YOUR GRANDFATHER

Names

Birthdate Birthplace

YOUR AUNTS

YOUR UNCLES

YOUR COUSINS

YOUR SISTERS & BROTHERS

YOUR MOTHER

Names

Birthdate Birthplace

Our family tree

Paternal

YOUR GREAT GRANDMOTHER

Names

Birthdate

Birthplace

YOUR GREAT GRANDFATHER

Names

Birthdate

Birthplace

YOUR GRANDMOTHER

Names

Birthdate *Birthplace*

YOUR GRANDFATHER

Names

Birthdate *Birthplace*

YOUR AUNTS

YOUR UNCLES

YOUR COUSINS

YOUR SISTERS & BROTHERS

YOUR FATHER

Names

Birthdate *Birthplace*

Our family history

Our origins...

Family names...

"You promised to tell me about your history, you know;" said Alice...

LEWIS CARROLL

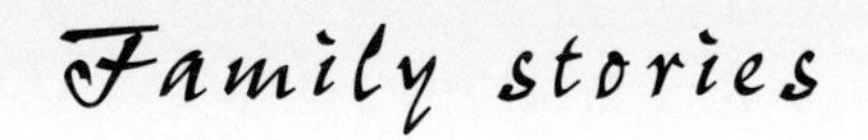

Family stories

"This here young lady", said the Gryphon,

"she wants for to know your history, she do"."I'll tell it her", said the Mock Turtle.

LEWIS CARROLL

Memories of my mother and father

(your great grandparents)

Mrs March wanted to talk of her father with the old man who had not forgotten him.

LOUISA MAY ALCOTT

She was singing in a low tone. I think I must have lain in her arms, and heard her singing so to me when I was but a baby. The strain was new to me, and yet it was so old that it filled my heart brimful, like a friend come back from a long absence.

CHARLES DICKENS

Memories of my grandparents

(your great great grandparents)

Her grandfather went to bed also before it was dark, for he always got up with the sun...

JOHANNA SPYRI

Music, when soft voices die,
Vibrates in the memory –

PERCY BYSSHE SHELLEY

Family photographs

[PHOTOGRAPH]

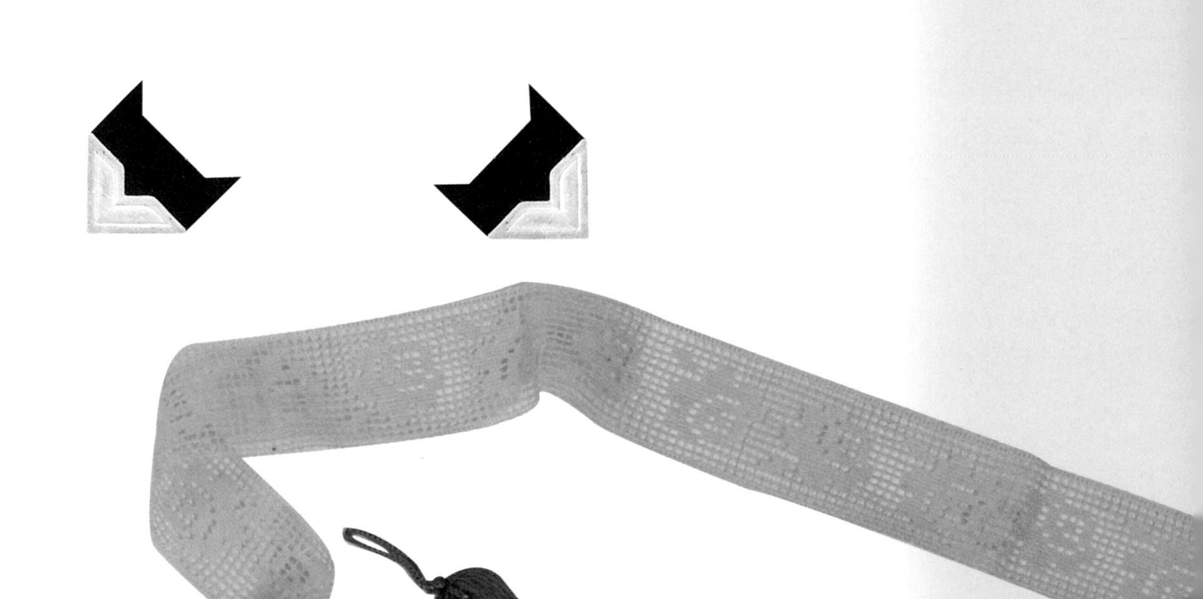

[PHOTOGRAPH]

I am the family face;
Flesh perishes, I live on,
Projecting trait and trace
Through time to times anon,
And leaping from place to place
Over oblivion.

THOMAS HARDY

My beginnings

I was born....

....

....

....

....

....

....

....

"Where do you come from?" said the Red Queen. "And where are you going?"

LEWIS CARROLL

Youth, what man's age is like to be doth show;
We may our ends by our beginnings know.

SIR JOHN DENHAM

Earliest memories

. . . .

. . . .

. . . .

. . . .

But for those first affections,
Those shadowy recollections,
Which, be they what they may,
Are yet the fountain light of all our day,
Are yet a master light of all our seeing.

WILLIAM WORDSWORTH

[PHOTOGRAPH]

O strengthen me, enlighten me!
I faint in this obscurity,
Thou dewy dawn of memory.

ALFRED LORD TENNYSON

When I was a girl

My recollections of childhood ....

....

....

Games I played.... ....

....

....

Books I read.... ....

....

....

Behold the child, by Nature's kindly law
Pleased with a rattle, tickled with a straw.

ALEXANDER POPE

Things I loved...

School days...

I found an old box hid away in a room,
And, lifting the lid open wide,
I found a little girl's pinafores hid
And worn-out shoes tucked under the lid,
And tattered old toys inside.

ANON

WHERE I GREW UP

My memories of home...

My favorite room....

Household curiosities....

Where I played.....

I remember, I remember
The house where I was born,
The little window where the sun
Came peeping in at Morn;

THOMAS HOOD

Special memories

I remember....

How dear to this heart are the
Scenes of my childhood,
When fond recollection presents them to view!
The orchard, the meadow, the deep-tangled wildwood,
And every loved spot which my infancy knew.

SAMUEL WOODWORTH

from my childhood

When the voices of children are heard on the green
And laughing is heard on the hill,
My heart is at rest within my breast
And everything else is still.

WILLIAM BLAKE

Photographs

[PHOTOGRAPH]

Photographs

[P H O T O G R A P H]

AS A YOUNG WOMAN...

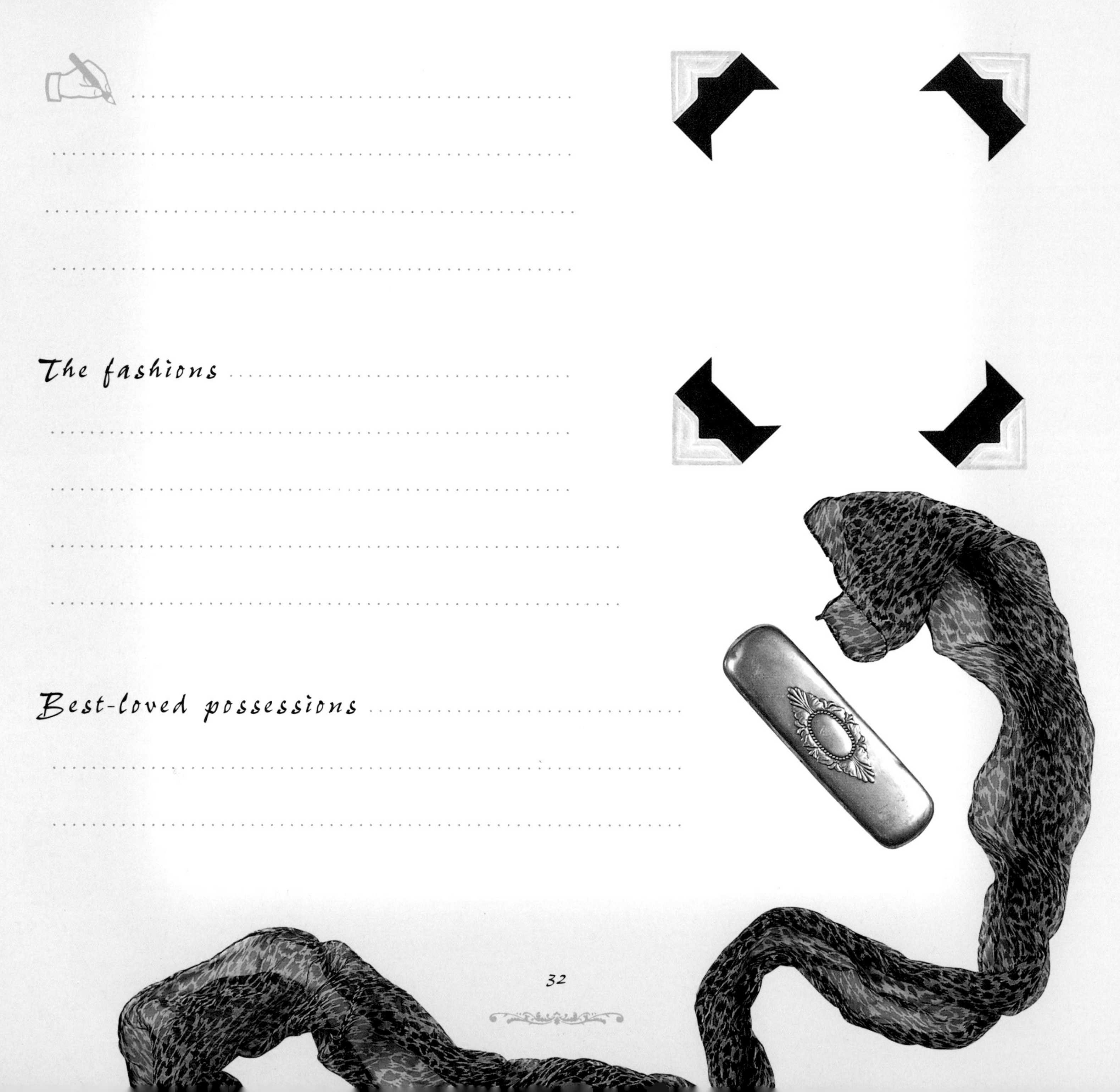

The fashions

Best-loved possessions

Memorable occasions

"You must have gloves, or I won't go," cried Meg, decidedly —
"Gloves are more important than anything else; you can't dance without them."

LOUISA MAY ALCOTT

Jo's nineteen hair-pins all seemed stuck straight into her head,
which was not exactly comfortable; but, dear me, let us be elegant or die.

LOUISA MAY ALCOTT

My favorite pastimes

Dramatic influences

Best loved books, music, movies and plays ....

A good book is the best of friends, the same to-day and forever.

MARTIN TUPPER

Stamp ALBUM

Other hobbies and interests

Of music Dr Johnson used to say that it was the only sensual pleasure without vice.

SAMUEL JOHNSON

For what's a play without a woman in it?

THOMAS KYD

REMEMBERING GOOD TIMES

Oft in the stilly night
Ere slumber's chain has bound me,
Fond Memory brings the light
of other days around me.

THOMAS MOORE

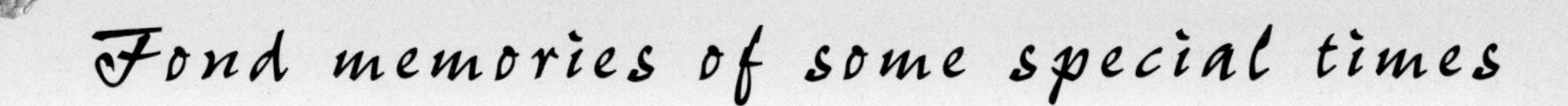

Sport that wrinkled Care derides,

And Laughter holding both his sides.

Come and trip it as ye go

On the light fantastic toe.

JOHN MILTON

ABOUT YOUR GRANDFATHER

Our meeting . . . .

Show me again just this:
The moment of that kiss
Away from the prancing folk, by the
strawberry-tree!

THOMAS HARDY

What attracted me to him . . . .

[PHOTOGRAPH]

Great times together

Don't ask what will happen tomorrow
Whatever the sum of days given to you,
Think of it as treasure,
And when you are young,
Never say no to dancing and sweet desire.

HORACE

Our wedding

Date

....

Time

....

Place

....

What I wore ....

....

....

Mercifully grant that we may grow old together.

BOOK OF TOBIT

My bouquet ....

....

....

PHOTOGRAPH

[P H O T O G R A P H]

And hand in hand, on the edge of the sand,

They danced by the light of the moon,

The moon,

The moon,

They danced by the light of the moon.

EDWARD LEAR

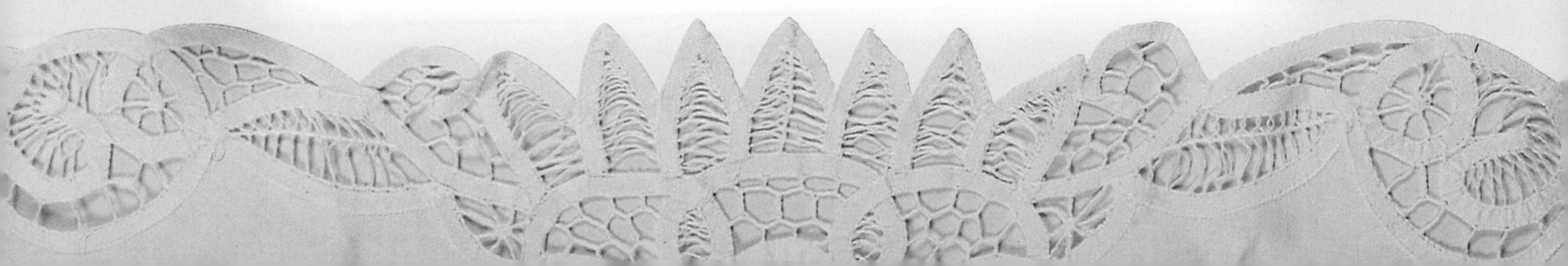

A HOME OF OUR OWN

Where we lived

Home is where the heart is.

About our home

We live in a numble abode.

CHARLES DICKENS

Home traditions

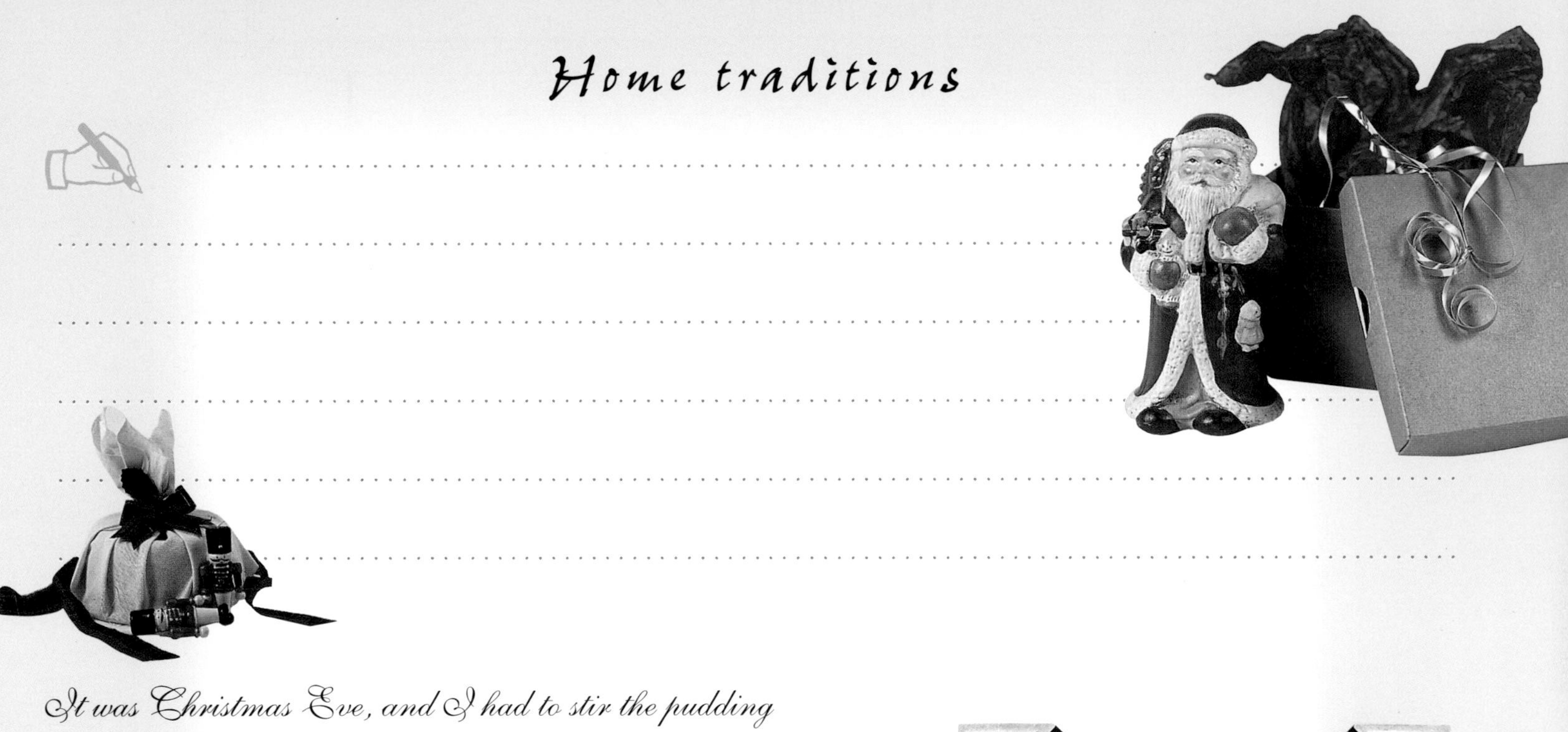

It was Christmas Eve, and I had to stir the pudding for next day, with a copper-stick, from seven to eight by the Dutch clock.

CHARLES DICKENS

[PHOTOGRAPH]

There was a good deal of laughing, and kissing, and explaining, in the simple, loving fashion which makes these home-festivals so pleasant at the time, so sweet to remember long afterward...

LOUISA MAY ALCOTT

Married life

How we lived

I'd rather see you poor men's wives,
if you were happy, beloved,
contented, than queens on thrones,
without self-respect and peace.

LOUISA MAY ALCOTT

Remembering good times

That best portion of a good man's life,
His little, nameless, unremembered acts
Of kindness and of love.

WILLIAM WORDSWORTH

FROM MY KITCHEN

Best recipes

"Now the cleverest thing of the sort that I ever did", he went on after a pause,
" was inventing a new pudding during the meat-course".

LEWIS CARROLL

FROM MY GARDEN

Garden recollections

Herbs & flowers

Time spent in my garden

How could such sweet and wholesome hours
Be reckoned, but with herbs and flowers.

ANDREW MARVELL

Becoming a mother

The pregnant me....

My children...

Birthdates...

Your children are not your children.
They are the sons and daughters
of life's longing for itself.

KAHLIL GIBRAN

My thoughts and reflections on motherhood

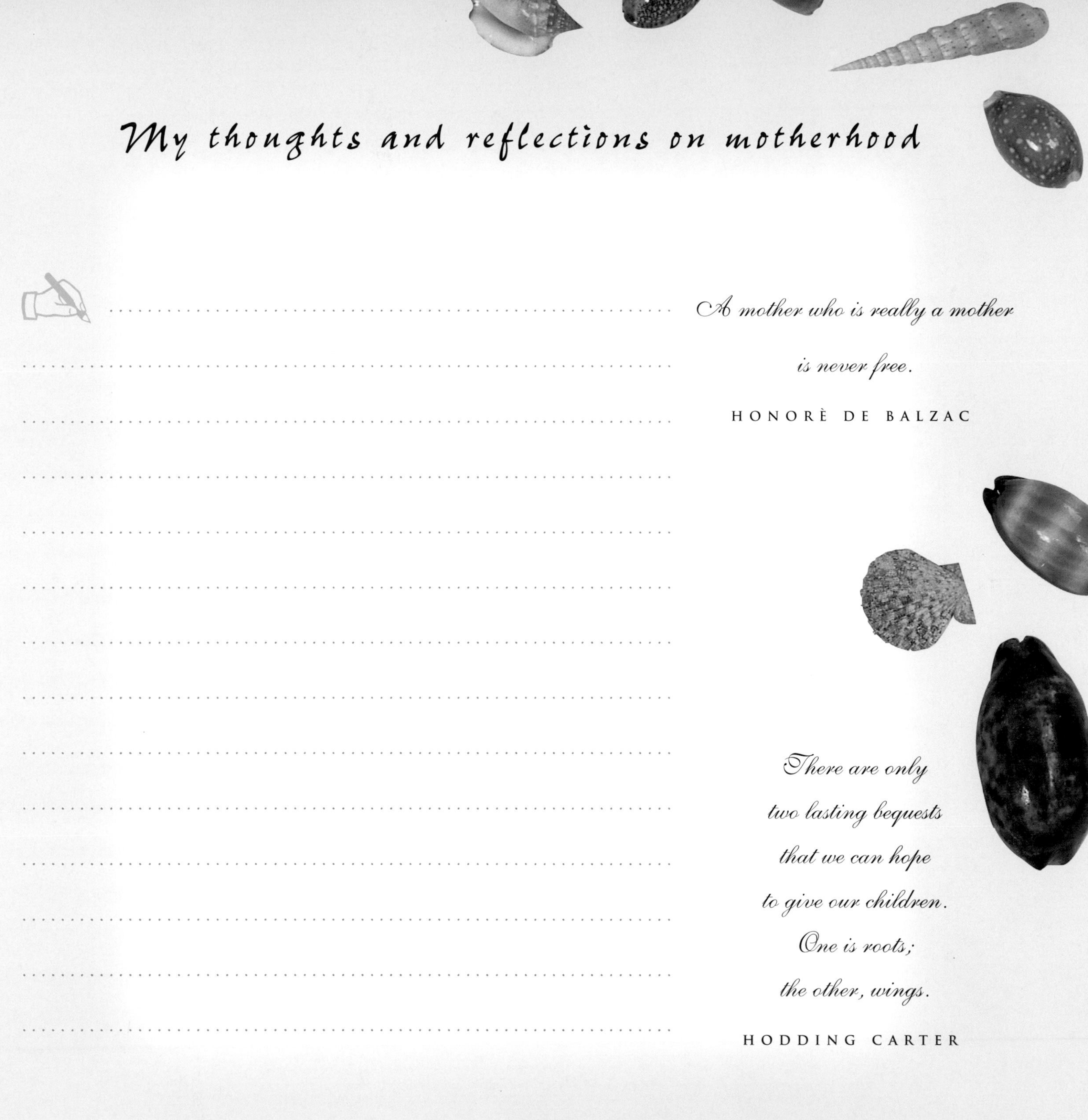

A mother who is really a mother
is never free.

HONORÈ DE BALZAC

There are only
two lasting bequests
that we can hope
to give our children.
One is roots;
the other, wings.

HODDING CARTER

About your mother and father

Names

Birthdates

Places of birth

Star signs

We are transfused into our children.

Fondest memories

Come to me, O ye children!
For I hear you at your play,
And the questions that perplexed me
Have vanished quite away.

HENRY WADSWORTH LONGFELLOW

Photographs

[PHOTOGRAPH]

Photographs

[PHOTOGRAPH]

The Childhood shows the man
As morning shows the day.

JOHN MILTON

PLACES I HAVE BEEN

My most memorable travels

The exhilaration of starting off on one's first long journey, young, ignorant, buoyant, expectant, is unlike anything else, unless it be youth itself, the real beginning of the real journey - life.

LUCY LARCOM, *A New England Girlhood*

Travel, in the younger sort, is a part of education;
in the elder, a part of experience.

FRANCIS BACON, *Essays of Travel*

I must go down to the seas again, to the vagrant gypsy life.

JOHN MASEFIELD

Stories from my life

"What do you want me to tell you?" she said.

FRANCES HODGSON BURNETT

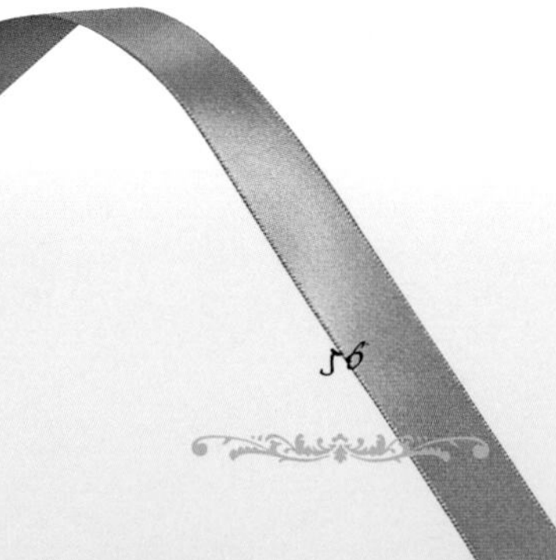

for you to share in

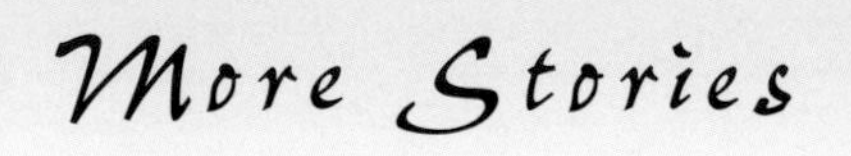

More Stories

and some unforgettable experiences

Of all the strange things that Alice saw in her journey Through the Looking Glass,
this was the one that she always remembered most clearly.

LEWIS CARROLL

My life's achievements

Great things are done when men and mountains meet;

WILLIAM BLAKE

Talent develops in quiet places, character in the full current of human life.

JOHANN WOLFGANG VON GOETHE

Things won are done; joy's soul lies in the doing.

WILLIAM SHAKESPEARE

Jo's ambition was to do something very splendid; what it was she had no idea, but left it for time to tell her.

LOUISA MAY ALCOTT

How life has changed

The more things change, the more they are the same.

ALPHONSE KARR

Life is a succession of lessons which must be lived to be understood.

RALPH WALDO EMERSON

The old order changeth, yeilding place to new,...

ALFRED LORD TENNYSON

'Ye can call it influenza if ye like...There was no influenza in my young days. We called a cold a cold.'

ARNOLD BENNETT

How you, my darling grandchild, enriched my life

I love my young and hopeful days dead and gone, in him.
I could'nt sell that love, and look in your bright face. It's a free gift.

CHARLES DICKENS

What you called your grandfather and I

THINGS YOU AND I SHARED

Family ties

Our similarities and differences

Features

Personality

Expressions

Times together

Adventures of Huckleberry Finn

bad fix—for the Sheriff 'll get 'em. Quick—hurry! I'll hunt the labboard side, you hunt the stabboard. You start at the raft, and—"

"Oh, my lordy, lordy! *Raf?* Dey ain' no raf' no mo', she done broke loose en gone!—en here we is!"

92

13 Escaping from the Wreck—The Watchman—Sinking

Well, I catched my breath and most fainted. Shut up on a wreck with such a gang as that! But it warn't no time to be sentimenter-ing. We'd *got* to find that boat, now—had to have it for ourselves. So we went a-quaking and shaking down the stabboard side and slow work it was, too—seemed a week before we got to th stern. No sign of a boat. Jim said he didn't believe he could any further—so scared he hadn't hardly any strength left, said. But I said come on, if we get left on this wreck, we ar a fix, sure. So on we prowled, again. We struck for the ster the texas, and found it, and then scrabbled along forward the skylight, hanging on from shutter to shutter, for the of the skylight was in the water. When we got pretty close cross-hall door, there was the skiff, sure enough! I cou barely see her. I felt ever so thankful. In another second

93

Experiencing each other

The fullness of your bliss, I feel - I feel it all.

WILLIAM WORDSWORTH

Photographs

[PHOTOGRAPH]

I love to gaze upon a child;
A young bud bursting into blossom.

CHARLES S. CALVERLEY

Photographs

[PHOTOGRAPH]

The colours of life in youth and age appear different,
as the face of nature in spring and winter.

SAMUEL JOHNSON

Treasured moments with you

Our favorite rhymes & stories

Our favorite songs

Our favorite games

YOUR EARLY YEARS

Child of the pure unclouded brow
And dreaming eyes of wonder!
Though time be fleet, and I and thou
Are half a life asunder,
Thy loving smile will surely hail
The love-gift of a fairy-tale.

LEWIS CARROLL

Treasured moments with you

I was there when

GROWING UP

A noontide have you been
in our twilight, and your
youth has given us dreams
to dream.

KAHLIL GIBRAN

O joy! that in our embers
Is something that doth live.

WILLIAM WORDSWORTH

WORDS OF WISDOM

The love we give away is the only love we keep.

ELBERT HUBBARD

The best way to make children good is to make them happy.

OSCAR WILDE

Our deeds still travel with us from afar,
And what we have been makes us what we are.

GEORGE ELIOT

Since we cannot get what we like, let us like what we can get.

SPANISH PROVERB

A change of fortune can make the strongest person need a weaker person's help.

AESOP'S FABLES

'Tis one thing to be tempted, Escalus,
Another thing to fall.

SHAKESPEARE

Great works are performed, not by strength, but perseverance.

SAMUEL JOHNSON

More words of wisdom

Be true to yourself

All things in moderation

Honesty is the best policy

Pride comes before a fall

Least said soonest mended

Laughter is the best medicine

Beauty comes from within

When one door closes another door opens

Forgive and forget

My words for you

What I wish for you

...he now rejoiced in his youth, because in many years much might be done.

SAMUEL JOHNSON

He who binds to himself a joy
Does the winged life destroy;
But he who kisses the joy as it flies
Lives in eternity's sunrise.

WILLIAM BLAKE

And alone and without his nest
Shall the eagle fly across the sun.

KAHLIL GIBRAN

I have spread my dreams under your feet;

W. B. YEATS

IMPORTANT THINGS FOR YOU TO REMEMBER

'...But I always want to know the things one shouldn't do'.

'So as to do them?' asked her aunt.

'So as to choose,' said Isabel.

HENRY JAMES

REMEMBER ME

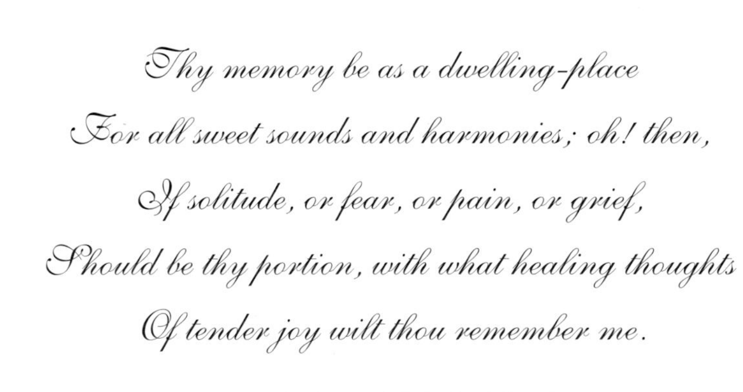

Thy memory be as a dwelling-place
For all sweet sounds and harmonies; oh! then,
If solitude, or fear, or pain, or grief,
Should be thy portion, with what healing thoughts
Of tender joy wilt thou remember me.

WILLIAM WORDSWORTH

The music in my heart I bore
Long after it was heard no more.

WILLIAM WORDSWORTH

[PHOTOGRAPH]